KT-492-359

THE PHYSICAL
BASIS OF MIND

THE PHYSICAL BASIS OF MIND

A Series of Broadcast Talks

EDITED BY
PETER LASLETT

BASIL BLACKWELL
OXFORD
1952

First printed, April, 1950
Fifth impression, September, 1952

Printed in Great Britain for Basil Blackwell & Mott, Limited
by A. R. Mowbray & Co. Limited in the City of Oxford

PREFATORY NOTE

THIS little book is a collection of talks originally delivered in the B.B.C. Third Programme, and subsequently printed in *The Listener*. The series was conceived and edited by a layman, one who has no claim to be a physician, a philosopher, or a scientist. The end in view was a conspectus of the evidence now available, and of the theories now being put forward, about what goes on in the body when men and animals are thinking. To be authoritative, such information had to come from the mouths of the men who themselves made the discoveries and had worked on the hypotheses. It had also to be presented in a form which was immediately intelligible not only to a lay editor, but to everybody else who felt that what was being studied in the laboratory in this field affected him. It was believed, moreover, that it would be both interesting and useful to have the opinions of philosophers on the evidence submitted in this way by the scientists.

Such a series of talks was bound to be an experiment in broadcasting if only because it was so ambitious. The difficulties were enhanced because of the technical terms used by the scientists and the unfamiliarity of their concepts. In reading the contributions it must be remembered that none of the speakers could assume that his hearers had listened to any of his predecessors, or possessed specialist knowledge of any kind. This accounts for a certain amount of repetitiveness. There was, moreover, no opportunity for consultation between the various contributors before individual talks were written, though Sir Charles Sherrington's introduction was sent to each of them when he was first approached. The personal attitude of the speakers towards the general problem of the physical basis of mind determined the form of each contribution, but the responsibility for the selection of topics and the general shape of the series must remain with the compiler.

Professor Alexander Kennedy of the University of Durham and Dr. John Bates of the National Hospital, Queen Square, have given important advice and help. I should like to acknowledge the patient collaboration of all the contributors in the original broadcasts, and also their permission to reprint the scripts. I should particularly like to record my gratitude to Sir Henry Dale, Professor Adrian, Dr. Wilder Penfield, and above all to Sir Charles Sherrington.

PETER LASLETT.

ST. JOHN'S COLLEGE,
    CAMBRIDGE.

TABLE OF CONTENTS

THE PHYSICAL BASIS OF MIND

I

INTRODUCTORY

By SIR CHARLES SHERRINGTON, O.M.

[Sir Charles Sherrington's broadcast was prefaced by a short address from Sir Henry Dale, O.M. He introduced him to his audience as 'a veteran of science, still in full mental vigour in his ninety-second year, the greatest physiologist alive to-day. He has been the chief pioneer of the experimental analysis of the central nervous system, and his book *The Integrative Action of the Nervous System* is one of the great classics of physiology and medical science.']

KNOWLEDGE of the physical basis of mind is making great strides in these days. Knowledge of the brain is growing, and our theme is almost equivalent to the physiology of the brain. Mind, meaning by that thoughts, memories, feelings, reasoning, and so on, is difficult to bring into the class of physical things. Physiology, a natural science, tends to be silent about all outside the physical. And so the study of the physical basis of mind suffers from falling between two stools.

As a scientific study, it began with observations—that loss of the brain produces loss of mind. But observation of mind is not so straightforward as might be thought. It is not safe even to suppose that mind is universally present in animal life. Most life is, I imagine, mindless, although the behaviour is purposeful. Mind is always an inference from behaviour, and that sometimes is difficult to interpret. It would seem that though there is matter which exists apart from mind, we know of no instance where mind exists apart from matter; that is, if we define 'mind' as we agreed to do.

That the brain is the bodily organ of the mind we have to accept as an established fact. It is perhaps somewhat surprising that the living brain is quite insensitive to handling, or cutting, or even searing with hot iron and so on. The modern surgeon has ascertained that. The most universal agent for provoking activity of nerve is the electric current, but, applied to the living brain, it fails to evoke any obvious effect except in a certain limited area, and there it provokes not 'thoughts,' but limited movements of the body. These movements do not seem 'willed' to the person experiencing them, although he or she perceives them. But the electric current, when applied to the naked human brain, does at times call up 'thoughts.' The experienced brain-surgeon, Professor Wilder Penfield, has examined this effect. He finds that at certain points of the brain surface an electric current will call up to the patient a familiar scene, not always quite the same scene.

There is a devastating disease of the brain called sleepy-sickness—not sleep*ing*-sickness which is something different. Sleepy-sickness, when the acute stage is passed, may leave behind it great mental irritability and revolt against ordinary conventions of society, even to violence. It is found that the sufferer can often be relieved of this perversion of mind by surgical operation on the brain. The surgeon cuts certain large bundles of nerve fibres connecting the front part of the brain with the rest of the brain—an operation called 'pre-frontal leucotomy.' As the patient gets well from the wound the condition of his personality is found to have improved; he often becomes quiet and reasonable, and remains so. Again it has been known for some years that electrical examination of the surface of the head detects electrical activity of a rhythmic kind going on almost continuously in the brain. Professor Adrian, who has studied this, will, I expect, tell us about it, and no one living is better able to do so.

The physical basis of mind encroaches more and more upon the study of mind, but there remain mental events which seem to lie beyond any physiology of the brain. When I turn my gaze skyward I see the flattened dome of sky and the sun's brilliant disc and a hundred other visible things underneath it. What are the steps which bring this about? A pencil of light from the sun enters the eye and is focused there on the retina. It gives rise to a change, which in turn travels to the nerve-layer at the top of the brain. The whole chain of these events, from the sun to the top of my brain, is physical. Each step is an electrical reaction. But now there succeeds a change wholly unlike any which led up to it, and wholly inexplicable by us. A visual scene presents itself to the mind; I *see* the dome of sky and the sun in it, and a hundred other visual things beside. In fact, I perceive a picture of the world around me. When this visual scene appears I ought, I suppose, to feel startled; but I am too accustomed to feel even surprised.

It is a far cry from an electrical reaction in the brain to suddenly seeing the world around one, with all its distances, its colours and chiaroscuro. Philosophers to-day, I fancy, incline to dividing the world of our experience into two sorts, a material and a spiritual. On the other hand, our scientists, I fancy, lean towards accepting mind itself as a form of energy. I would like to hear Lord Samuel on this. The Victorian era witnessed violent divergences of doctrine upon it. John Stuart Mill protested against those who supposed that, for seeing, the possession of an eye is a necessity. On the other hand, the oracular Professor Tyndall, presiding over the British Association at Belfast, told his audience that as the bile is a secretion of the liver, so the mind is a secretion of the brain.

Aristotle, 2,000 years ago, was asking how is the mind attached to the body. We are asking that question still.

II

WHAT HAPPENS WHEN WE THINK

By E. D. ADRIAN, O.M.

I SUPPOSE everyone who tries to understand what is going on in the brain must suffer from time to time from the feeling that he has chosen a really insoluble problem, not merely a very difficult one. Heaven knows, it is going to be difficult enough to make an intelligible picture of the working of an organ which has millions and millions of parts and is responsible for all the complicated things we can do: but difficulties of that sort could be faced. The real trouble comes from the feeling that there may be an important part of the picture which can never be fitted in, however long we may work at it.

Sherrington explained why we should have these misgivings. The part of our picture of the brain which may always be missing is, of course, the part which deals with the mind, the part which ought to explain how a particular pattern of nerve impulses can produce an idea; or the other way round, how a thought can decide which nerve cells are to come into action. It is a very old difficulty and nowadays some of the philosophers tell us that if we look at it in the right way it is not as serious as it seems. But the physiologist cannot look at it except as a natural scientist and at present that seems almost certain to lead him into trouble. My own feeling is that before the trouble comes to a head it will have been solved by some enlargement of the boundaries of natural science, by the progress of psychology, for instance. In fact, psychology can scarcely get along without coming to terms with the relation of body and mind.

So for the present we can set aside these misgivings and go on trying to find out what sort of physical and chemical changes are taking place in the brain when the mind is at work. There has been some progress in this field and it is bound to make the ultimate problem more definite even though it may never lead to the final solution.

There is one point about which we still know very little indeed, and it is so important that I ought to mention it at the outset. It concerns memory, learning and forming habits. We really do not know what sort of change takes place in the brain when a memory is established. Animals with much simpler nervous systems than ours can learn, and it seems reasonable to suppose that some kind of change has been impressed on their nervous system when they do, but so far we can only list the kind of change which might happen, which might make the nerve cells conduct more easily in certain directions. We have no direct evidence to show what really does happen. Of course, there is a good deal of evidence about the way in which memories are formed, there is all Pavlov's work on conditioned reflexes, for instance, on learning in animals. We know that it takes a few seconds for a memory to be securely fixed in the brain. We know that some parts of the brain can be removed without causing any loss of memory and that other parts are best left alone. But what actually happens in the nerve cells is still quite uncertain. And as all our thoughts depend on what we have learnt, we shall not know much about what happens when we think until we have found out more about what happens in the nervous system when we learn something.

Now let me pass from that to say what we do know. You must think of the brain as a very large sheet of nerve cells, so large that it is thrown into folds to make it fit inside the skull. It communicates with the sense organs and with the muscles by long nerve fibres— threads which have the power of conducting signals very rapidly. There are about 10,000,000,000 nerve cells in the brain, and they are connected by an inter-lacing network of threads so that a cell is rarely active without influencing its neighbours. The essential activity seems to consist in a sudden change in the cell surface which allows a momentary escape of some of the molecules. This surface change can be repeated at very short intervals so that the cell may become active and inactive as often as fifty times a second, and each time it becomes active an impulse will pass out from the cell to its neighbours or further afield to other parts of the central nervous system.

To maintain all this activity the brain needs a large blood supply to bring it oxygen and foodstuffs—sugar particularly—and the blood supply cannot be inter-rupted for more than a few seconds without bringing the machinery to a standstill. That happens some-times in the ordinary fainting fit when our mind goes out of action because the brain has not enough blood supply to keep the nerve cells working.

A great deal is already known about the structure

of the brain, the routes by which the nervous signals enter and leave it, and the way in which one part of the sheet of nerve cells is connected with another. And we know something of the functions of the different parts from observing what happens when they are damaged. For instance, injury in a certain region on the left side will cause aphasia; that is, difficulty in using words: injury in another region will paralyse the hand, and so on. But to find out what is actually going on in the cells at any moment we must use a more direct method, which depends on the fact that whenever nerve cells or fibres are active they produce electrical effects—rapid changes of potential corresponding to the changes in the surface membrane.

The electrical changes are very small, and they can only be detected by placing electrodes in contact with the cells or with the fluids and tissues close to them, but nowadays it is a simple matter to amplify them until they are large enough to be recorded photographically: it can be done with a cathode ray oscillograph, or a record can be traced in ink on a moving strip of paper. Records of these electrical changes show that the messages which are sent into the brain from the sense organs are made up of repeated impulses in the nerve fibres—the impulse is a wave of activity due to a sudden change in the surface of the fibre sweeping down it at a rate of about a hundred feet a second. The impulses usually follow one another in a rapid series—from ten to two hundred a second, or more— and a good many nerve fibres are usually needed to carry the message.

So when we see a light or hear a sound, the first thing that happens in the brain is the arrival of a great many nerve impulses. The messages that come in are all very much alike, but they arrive by different routes. Those from the eye are sent to the back of the brain and their arrival there makes us see; those from the ear go to the side and when they arrive there we hear something. The arrival of the signal is only the first stage: if the nerve cells of the brain were put out of action by an anaesthetic, the impulses might still reach them but we should neither see nor hear, we should be unconscious. We can only be conscious when our brain is in the normal waking state, and in this state many of the nerve cells are in constant activity, whether signals are arriving or not. A record from the surface of the brain would show electrical oscillations taking place all the time, oscillations due to groups of nerve cells continually discharging. In fact, one may liken the conscious brain to a sheet of water constantly disturbed by the wind, with all sorts of ripples on its surface. When we go to sleep the ripples, the electric waves, die down and mental activity ceases, though there is some return of activity in the nerve cells if we begin to dream. A signal coming in from a sense organ to the waking brain will disturb the ripples like a pebble thrown into the water. But the surprising thing is that a disturbance of this kind in one part of a sheet of nerve cells should make us see a light, and that the same kind of disturbance in another part should make us hear a sound.

Unfortunately, most of these electrical patterns cannot be recorded properly unless the brain is exposed so that the electrodes can be brought very close to the nerve cells. The potential changes are too small to be detected through the skull. But there is one kind of nerve cell activity which can be followed more easily because the potential waves are larger and simpler. It is the activity known as the alpha rhythm. The electroencephalogram—the record of brain potentials from the scalp—was first investigated by Hans Berger twenty years ago. He found that in most people sitting with the eyes closed and the attention relaxed there were regular potential changes at the surface of the head, changes of about a twentieth of a millivolt occurring at the rate of about ten a second. The rhythm takes place in the nerve cells over a considerable part of the brain surface; but it always stops if the subject opens his eyes and looks at something or if his attention is arrested by an unusual noise or concentrated on a problem—on mental arithmetic, for instance.

To give such large, regular waves many of the nerve cells must have become linked together so that they are all active and inactive simultaneously. This can only happen when they are not disturbed by signals coming into the brain, and it looks as though the rhythm means that the cells are marking time, as it were, ready to play an active part when they are needed, but not in use at the moment. All manner of thoughts and images may be coming and going in the mind when the eyes are closed, but unless they arrest the attention a considerable part of the brain surface remains free to go on with its regular beat.

Ordinary casual thinking, then, does not involve widespread changes in cell activity, but really concentrated thinking does, for then the cells have to stop their uniform rhythm. Probably they break up into groups, some of which are more and some less active, but records from the surface of the head can only show a gross change like the disappearance of the waves. There are other gross changes which can be made to occur in rather artificial conditions: for instance, if you look at a flickering light the nerve cells at the back of the brain will start responding at the same rate as the flicker, and similar effects have been found recently with other kinds of sensation.

So records made through the skull cannot tell us what the subject is thinking about, but they can tell whether he is concentrating his attention; and, if he is looking at a flickering light, they can tell us how rapidly it is flickering. That is at least a beginning, though it may be some time before we can go much further. We know something about the preliminary stages in seeing a light, the arrival of the signals from the eyes and the first response of the brain cells to these signals. But when the pebble is thrown into the sheet of water the ripples which it sets up will spread widely, and will start all sorts of complicated patterns with the other ripples which were going on before. We shall have to trace out the complex patterns of nerve cell activity which are set going by the signal, and the human brain is so large that a complete survey may be out of the question.

But I think there is a reasonable hope that we may be able to sort out the particular activities which coincide with quite simple mental processes like seeing or hearing. At all events that is the first thing the physiologist must do if he is trying to find out what happens when we think and how the mind is influenced by what goes on in the brain.

III

THE STRUCTURE OF THE BRAIN AND THE PROCESS OF THINKING

By W. E. LE GROS CLARK

SUPPOSE we begin by considering the sort of mental impressions which we get when we examine, say, an orange. Our mental impressions depend, in the first instance, on the fact that a number of different sense organs which we possess are thrown into activity. From each of these sense organs bundles of exceedingly fine nerve fibres emerge to connect them with what is termed the central nervous system—that is to say, the brain and spinal cord.

When a sense organ is excited into activity, this activity is signalled to the central nervous system by nervous impulses which are transmitted at a high speed along the nerve fibres. So when we examine an orange with our hands, it excites numerous minute sense organs scattered in and underneath the skin, some of which are particularly sensitive to touch, others to pressure, and others to temperature and so forth. The signals which reach the spinal cord from such sense organs are ultimately carried up to the brain, and they make it possible for us to recognize the shape and size of the orange, and the texture of its surface. At the same time, light rays reflected from the surface of the orange may stimulate the sensitive membrane in the eye, the retina—and immediately hundreds of thousands of nervous impulses speed along the optic nerve to the brain. These provide the information whereby we can distinguish all the details of the appearance of an orange—such as its form and colour. Again, molecular particles, diffusing into the surrounding air from the surface of the orange, may excite the lining membrane inside the nose, and nervous impulses which connect this membrane with the brain will then permit us to recognize its characteristic smell.

But all these nervous impulses do not give rise to a conscious sensation just as soon as they reach some region of the central nervous system. When the sense organs of touch in the skin of the hand are excited into activity, the signals which are transmitted from them first enter the spinal cord, which is an important part of the central nervous system, but if the connections between the spinal cord and the brain are interrupted, the touch is not felt just by means of the spinal cord alone. Somehow or other the signals must be transmitted up the spinal cord to the brain before a sensation is experienced.

As a matter of fact, many of the sensory nerve fibres of the spinal nerves end almost as soon as they enter the spinal cord. They end by breaking up into fine networks which penetrate among clusters of nerve cells of the cord itself, and come into direct contact with the cells themselves. From these cells a new lot of nerve fibres take their origin and stream up the spinal cord to the brain. In other words, the signals which are in the first place transmitted to the spinal cord from the skin are passed on to groups of cells in the cord and relayed through them up to the brain. Or suppose we take the case of impulses carried along the optic nerve from the eye. The majority of these end in a mass of nerve cells at the base of the brain. But they do not *there* give rise to a visual sensation. It is only when the impulses have been relayed from the base of the brain to a much more complicated mechanism in the grey matter on the *surface* of the brain—the cerebral cortex— that a conscious sensation becomes possible.

It is the anatomist's task—and a very formidable task it is—to trace out the pathways which the nervous impulses take. I have described how they reach the central nervous system from the various sense organs of the body and how they are eventually conveyed to those complicated parts of the brain upon whose proper functioning normal mental experience seems to depend. These pathways are formed by bundles of nerve fibres. The fibres are microscopic in size so that they cannot be dissected out with scalpel and forceps, except in a very few instances when they form large compact and more or less isolated bundles. They have to be studied under the high power of the microscope.

Now if you look at a thin slice of brain tissue under the microscope—a slice which has been stained by special dyes to make the fibres stand out clearly—you get a most confused picture. Thousands and thousands of nerve fibres can be seen running apparently in all directions—intertwining and crossing each other in a most complicated pattern. Indeed, it would appear to be an impossible task to trace any single group of nerve fibres to its ultimate destination through such a labyrinth. Fortunately for the anatomist, however, there are things which make the task less difficult than it otherwise would be. One is that, if a nerve fibre is interrupted by some injury, it undergoes a process of degeneration and crumbles into little fragments which finally disappear altogether. By applying special staining methods it is possible to distinguish degenerating fibres from the normal fibres with which they may be intermingled.

Suppose, therefore, you have the opportunity of studying the brain of somebody who has died after a severe injury which has severed the optic nerve on its way from the eye to the brain. Then, by using the special staining methods, you can follow the crumbling fibres of the optic nerve into the brain and find out exactly where they end. You can do the same thing even if only a few fibres from one particular spot in the retina have been interrupted. In this way it has been found that each local spot in the retina is linked with a correspondingly local group of cells at the base of the brain. This is the orderly arrangement which ultimately makes it possible for us to distinguish the relative position in space of any object which comes within our field of vision. Now if we want to find out the pathways along which signals from the retina are relayed on to the cerebral cortex, or surface layer of grey matter, we can do so by studying the brain in cases where some injury has interrupted *those* pathways either partially or completely.

Work like this is tedious, and there are involved all kinds of technical difficulties. But, by making use of such methods, the connections between one part of the central nervous system and another is being worked out bit by bit—for example, the pathways along which different kinds of sensory nervous impulses come to be finally distributed to the more highly organized parts

of the brain. Incidentally, also, by following pathways
in this manner, we can often get some clue to the extent
to which they separate or combine with each other. In
the one case opportunity is provided for the sensory
impulses which are carried along these pathways to
become sorted out into different categories; in the other
case, the opportunity is provided for impulses from
diverse sources to interact with each other. It is
elementary mechanisms of this kind which ultimately
make it possible for us to discriminate between one
sensation and another, or to integrate sensations of
various qualities so that we are able to form a mental
impression of an object as a whole.

Another thing which helps the work of the anatomist
is the tendency for those nerve fibres which carry
impulses concerned with the same kind of function to
run together in bundles. These bundles—or fibre
tracts, as they are called—are in some cases sufficiently
well defined to be identified and traced for some distance under the microscope, particularly if they are
undergoing disintegration as the result of some injury.
The sensory roots of the spinal nerves contain fibres
carrying impulses related to many kinds of sensations—
such as touch, pressure, heat, cold, and pain. Before
they reach the spinal cord, these fibres are all mixed
up. But as soon as they enter the spinal cord, they sort
themselves out in a remarkable way, so that the
impulses which are eventually carried up to the brain
become segregated into a number of different bundles.
An example of this is the impulses which produce a
sensation of pain. They are conveyed up the spinal
cord in a bundle which is quite well localized on each
side near the surface. Indeed, it is possible in special

circumstances to cut this tract as a surgical operation in order to prevent the patient from feeling pain in certain regions of the body—without at the same time seriously interfering with other kinds of sensation. Similarly, there are other tracts (or bundles of fibres) passing up the spinal cord in other positions, carrying impulses which permit us to appreciate the hotness or coldness of any object which we may handle, or to perceive the lightest touch on any part of the body. By following these tracts one by one, we are beginning to find where the impulses concerned with different sensations finally end. And we are beginning—but only just beginning—to get some sort of idea what is the final destination in the brain which they must reach if they are going to give rise to a conscious sensation.

Now let us take a look at this brain as a whole. A human brain weighs about fifty ounces, and most of it is made up of two large oval masses, side by side, called the cerebral hemispheres. These are connected together across the middle line by a bridge of nerve fibres which allows them to work in harmony with each other. From the middle of the base of the brain there comes down a stalk-like mass of nervous substance— the 'brain-stem'—through which the cerebral hemispheres above are linked up with the spinal cord below. The brain-stem is largely made up of great numbers of ascending fibre tracts along which signals from sense organs over most of the body are transmitted up to the cerebral hemispheres. It also contains important descending, or motor tracts, whereby impulses can be sent down from controlling centres in the brain by means of which are initiated movements of muscles and so on.

C

The surface of each cerebral hemisphere is corrugated to form a complex pattern of convolutions. The complexity of the pattern varies very much in mammals of different species: it is particularly marked in the higher mammals, such as monkeys and apes and, of course, even more so in man. If you cut a brain into slices, you will see that the whole surface of the cerebral hemisphere is covered by a thin layer of grey matter, the cerebral cortex. It is the numerous corrugations of the cortex which form the convolutions seen on the surface of the brain—and by becoming folded in this manner, the cortex enormously increases its extent. If the cortex is viewed under the microscope, it is seen to be composed of incredible numbers of densely packed nerve cells pervaded by a close-meshed feltwork of fibres. Some of these fibres have come up from lower levels of the central nervous system, carrying to the cortex impulses which have originated in all the various kinds of sense organs: others run from one part of the cortex to another—the so-called association fibres—and make it possible for different regions of the cortex to work in harmony with each other. Still other fibres run down from the cortex to motor mechanisms in lower levels of the central nervous system and make it possible for movements to be initiated and controlled under the influence of cortical activity.

Beneath the surface layers of cerebral cortex, the brain consists largely of pulpy white matter. Under the microscope, this is found to be composed of compact formations of nerve fibres running in many different directions. Embedded in the white matter—near the base of the brain—are some solid masses of grey matter of various kinds. We will refer to only one of these—the oval masses (one on either side of the mid-line) which comprise what is called the thalamus. The thalamus is made up of numerous groups of nerve cells, and its importance from our point of view is that it comprises a series of relay stations through which most sensory impulses must pass before they can reach the cerebral cortex. One group of cells in the thalamus (arranged in a rather intricate pattern of layers) passes on signals from the eye to a local area of cortex at the very back end of the brain. Another group serves to transmit impulses from the ears to another local area of cortex. Still another group relays the impulses which originate in the sense organs of the skin to its own particular cortical area. Now these groups of cells are more than simple relay stations—they are also 'sorting stations' which allow for the resorting of the incoming impulses so that they are then projected on to the cerebral cortex in a new kind of pattern. It is now beginning to appear that the discriminatory powers of the mind (that is, our capacity to distinguish different elements of sensation) may depend very much on the nature of those patterns—and it is the anatomist's job to map them out so far as his technical methods allow him to do so.

If the visual cortex receiving impulses relayed to it from the retina is destroyed by injury, we no longer have any conscious sensation of sight. If the auditory cortex receiving impulses relayed from the organ of hearing is entirely destroyed, we no longer have any conscious sensation of sound. So it looks as though the anatomical mechanisms in the cortex have an intimate relationship to our capacity for conscious perception. But it does not follow that as soon as sensory impulses impinge upon their particular local areas of the cortex they *immediately* give rise to an actual sensation. Probably they must spread widely throughout the brain before this can happen. Take the impulses from the retina, for example. We have seen that after these have been sorted out in the thalamus they are relayed to a local area of cortex at the back end of the brain. We now know that there are anatomical pathways by which they can be further distributed from that area to a narrow surrounding strip of cortex. Now, as soon as they reach this surrounding area, they are in a position to influence the activity of the brain as a whole, for from this narrow strip more relays of fibres arise which pass to deep-seated centres of grey matter near the base of the brain. These deep-seated centres of grey matter in their turn appear to contain quite fundamental mechanisms whereby the activity of the brain as a whole can be immediately modulated.

I have a hunch about this arrangement. It seems to me likely that the initiation of a visual sensation coincides with and is occasioned by the arrival of the retinal impulses at that strip of cortex through which these deep centres are thrown into activity. I must confess, though, that it is no more than a hunch, for there is as yet no conclusive evidence to support such an idea. But it seems to me that such evidence might eventually be obtained if the physiologist and psychologist can find a sufficiently accurate method of estimating the time which occurs between the presentation of a visual image to the retina and its conscious perception by the mind. For we know something of the rate at which impulses travel along nerve fibres, and also of the time involved in the transmission of the

impulses from one relay centre to another. The difficulty, however, is that the time intervals are so short—
a matter of thousandths of a second.

There is another interesting point for the anatomist
about the cerebral cortex; it has not the same structure
throughout. On the contrary, it can be divided up
into a large number of different areas, each of which
is to be distinguished by its characteristic structure.
There is increasing evidence that this structural
differentiation of the cortex in some cases betokens a
corresponding functional differentiation, for different
areas have different arrangements of fibre connections
with other parts of the brain. There was at one time
a good deal of criticism of this conception of functional
localization in the cortex, on the grounds that any form
of mental experience must necessarily involve the
activity of the brain as a whole. But, in fact, there is no
antithesis between these ideas. For, as I have just
mentioned in reference to the visual area of the cortex,
each anatomical area is linked by association fibres
with certain other cortical areas, and some of the latter
have direct connections with the deep masses of grey
matter through which the activity of the brain as a
whole can be immediately influenced. In fact, it is one
of the remarkable features of the cerebral cortex that it
combines so efficiently in one organization the machinery for analysing incoming impulses, and also the
machinery which permits their immediate interaction
and integration.

The outstanding feature in the evolution of man
from lower animals has been the progressive expansion
of the brain relatively to the size of the body, and it is
interesting to note that this expansion has to a con-

siderable extent involved the surface grey matter of the cerebral cortex, and the other parts of the brain directly connected with it. The very intricacy of the organization of the cerebral cortex permits a far wider range of actions and reactions in response to sensory impulses than the simpler organization of the more primitive centres of the brain. For while the primitive centres can only provide for inborn and automatic types of behaviour following a set pattern, the evolutionary development of the cerebral cortex makes possible the emergence of an intelligent type of behaviour which is individually modifiable and thus susceptible to educational influence. Now, with the progressive expansion of the cortex during evolution, centres of functional control which were originally located in more primitive parts of the brain have gradually become transferred up to the cortical level of the brain.

This transference from the lower levels to the higher is rather well illustrated by comparing the visual centres in the brain of the rat with those in the brain of man. A rat whose visual cortex has been destroyed can still make very good use of its eyesight—it can judge distance and direction accurately in jumping from one platform to another, and it can distinguish between different intensities of light. On the other hand, the destruction of the visual cortex in a man renders him completely and permanently blind. In the rat it is clear that many visual functions are still carried out by primitive centres in the brain-stem, and because of this the ways in which a rat can react to a visual stimulus are quite restricted. In man these functions have all been taken over by the cortex, and it is in relation to this fact that the range of his reactions to a visual stimulus is practically limitless.

There is reason to suppose that this phenomenon of the corticalization of brain function (as it is called) is not only an essential preliminary for the development of all those complicated mental processes which are distinctive of man among all other mammals. It also provides the anatomical machinery through which the conscious control of behaviour is made possible.

The size of the brain in proportion to the body-weight is, of course, one of the distinctive features of human anatomy. Its weight is two or three times that of the largest ape, the gorilla, and it seems to have taken a matter of several million years for man to achieve such a prodigious development of his brain. On the other hand, the fossil evidence indicates that the human brain has not appreciably changed in its size for about 200,000 years. There seems to be no evidence that man's brain is undergoing any further evolutionary expansion—or that it is even likely to do so. But it may well be argued that there are still tremendous opportunities for us to make evolutionary advances by learning how to make much fuller use of the brain with which we have already been equipped. It is an instructive fact that the size of our brains to-day shows an astonishing range of individual variation, and yet it has not been possible within wide limits to relate these differences to differences in intellectual capacity. A genius may have a brain of average size—or even rather smaller than average size—and no anatomist (even with the aid of the microscope) has yet been able to show any consistent difference between the intrinsic structure of the brain of a genius and the brain of a man of average intelligence. On anatomical grounds, therefore, it would seem that the main asset of the man of genius is not that he has been provided (ready made, so to speak) with a bigger and more elaborate brain, but that, in some way or another, he has got the knack of using the ordinary kind of human brain much more efficiently than most of us are able to do. It is an intriguing problem to consider how he acquires this knack!

In conclusion, I might emphasize—though perhaps it is not really necessary to do so—that the anatomist is primarily concerned with the study of the brain as the material substratum of mental processes. No more than the physiologist is he able even to suggest how the physico-chemical phenomena associated with the passage of nervous impulses from one part of the brain to another can be translated into a mental experience. But, by the study of the structural organization of the brain, and by observing the effects of a local disturbance of this structure on the working of the mind, it is becoming possible to define in more and more detail the particular anatomical dispositions which appear to be necessary as a basis for mental activity, or perhaps I should say, for the manifestations of mental activity.

IV

THE MECHANISM OF THOUGHT: THE MIND AND THE CALCULATING MACHINE

By S. ZUCKERMAN

IN his introduction Sir Charles Sherrington reminded us that physiology, as a natural science, is only concerned with physical matters, and that mind is an inference from behaviour. Both he and Professor Adrian also indicated that there may be mental events which lie outside any possible explanation of the way the brain functions. While this is a question essentially for philosophers, it is necessary—in my view—that the physiologist and anatomist should be aware of the way they define mind, however vague it is. It matters a great deal whether mind is regarded as something which is distinct from, and which animates the body—or whether the word is thought of as a generic term to cover such processes as feeling, thinking, remembering, perceiving, and so on. If mind is conceived of as something which interacts with body—or as some parallel manifestation to body—the scientist may be misled into trying to solve problems which may prove unreal. For example, I'm not convinced about the validity of the proposition—raised by Professor Le Gros Clark—that some parts of the brain have the special function of transforming measurable electrical impulses into consciousness.

If, on the other hand, we take mind as a verbal cloak for such processes as perceiving, abstracting, and reasoning, and focus our attention on these, we are in a better position to see how far any of them—as processes —can be explained in physical terms.

Those who have preceded me in this symposium have already described the physiological events which underlie perception. I therefore take it that we know roughly what happens when our sense organs are stimulated by the environmental changes to which they respond, and about the passage of electrical impulses in the nervous system. Perception is the process by which we become aware of changes in our internal and external environments. In less evolved forms of life its mechanisms are few and simple. In ourselves they are very specialized, and each of our main senses—such as sight and hearing—has a wide spectrum of sensitivity. It is this which allows us to make fine differentiations of our external world, and to respond in a variety of ways to these differentiations.

Organisms adjust themselves to their environments through the reactions which follow perception. The hungry animal prowls until it senses food, and having satisfied itself, resumes a new equilibrium in its environment. A man sees or hears a car rushing at him, and he jumps aside. Simple reactions like these are the bricks of the learning process, and learning can occur in probably all organisms. A worm put in the stem of a glass tube shaped like a Y will always go up the right-hand limb of the Y if it receives an electric shock every time it previously moved into the left limb. A hungry dog's mouth waters if food is placed in front of it. If food is produced and a bell is also sounded it will not be long before the animal's mouth waters when the bell is rung in the absence of food.

These are simple examples of the process of conditioning. Complicated responses can also be conditioned. The process is associated with emotional tone, success leading either to satisfaction or to an avoidance of discomfort or injury. We know a great deal about the characteristics of conditioning, and it is the basis of what is called trial-and-error learning. Some students also believe in the existence of another kind of learning called learning by 'insight'—a word which is used to describe the apparently sudden appreciation of the solution to problems. The relationship between this kind of learning and trial-and-error or conditioned response learning is, however, by no means clear.

Whether the two are related or distinct, learning is not a series of specific responses to individual sensory experiences—that is, to specific and absolute events in our environment. It has a more general character. For example, we know a table to be a table from whatever angle it is viewed, whatever its size or colour. Animals do the same, responding in the same way in spite of what seems to be considerable changes in the stimulus pattern. Furthermore, we can transfer a stimulus pattern from one to another of our senses. If we feel a coin in the dark, we know what it is and can transfer the sense of it, say, to our vision. A dog seems to build an impression of his master either from a sight of him in the distance, from the sound of his voice, or from his smell.

During our development, then, we establish general types of response which are related to general types of situation, and we learn to respond to a new situation with the type of response which experience has shown to be most suitable to that type of situation.

Both perception and learning are characteristics of all living matter. They are essential parts of the processes we understand by the term mind, but, by themselves, they do not presuppose mind.

The physical sciences do not seem to have advanced far enough to define the actual physical changes which underlie the processes of learning. Even the most powerful instruments of research cannot help us at all here. One important view, however, is that previous stimulation of a group of nerve cells and fibres—which has led to a state of satisfaction—increases its sensitivity to further stimulation of a like kind, the change taking place essentially at the synapses—the regions where nerve cells make contact with one another. But this explanation may be too rigid. We cannot suppose that each nerve cell is concerned in only one process of learning.

Whatever the physical process may be, it clearly also applies to the process of remembering. In remembering, past feelings and actions are evoked, and modified, by new things that are seen, or sensed in some other way. This kind of memory apparently occurs in most organisms. But because we humans use symbolic language, our own memory also works independently of immediate environmental control. No one knows the physical basis of this particularly human capacity. I have already said that the perceptions to which organisms adjust by learning are usually relational attributes of the environment, and not a series of absolute qualities. This so-called 'gestalt' or configuration perception is clearly an essential part of the abstractive process which underlies symbolic processes of communication. But while we share this perceptual process with animals, the use of language and number symbols—both written and spoken—seems to be our own particular characteristic, and the one to which we owe our dominance in the world of living things. We all know that animals lack speech and language; they also seem incapable of making number abstractions. Some years ago, two of my students tested this out. They tried in carefully controlled experiments to discover whether monkeys and apes understand what we seem to do by number. But it became more than clear that while they could tell the difference between one and two black circles— or any other set of convenient signs—the animals didn't realize there was a similar numerical quality in the different sets of signs used. Their failure was in isolating the number concept from the perceptual background in which it appeared, and in analysing it into its constituent units. The basis of our thinking and reasoning powers is our capacity for such kinds of abstraction and for mastering many kinds of symbolic process.

Now while it is not yet possible to define in physical terms the processes which mind connotes, we know some of the physical factors which modify their expression. For example, a rare hereditary change in a single one of the genes, as we call those elements which control heredity, will turn a normal humanbeing into a lunatic with a brain about the size of an ape's. Another rare hereditary condition—also associated with lunacy—is marked by an inability of the body to handle a particular constituent in our food—phenylalanine. In this case the failure of the brain to function normally is presumably due to a dietary and metabolic disorder. Advanced alcoholism and drug addiction also affect our mental processes: again, they can be severely affected by head injuries. Knowledge about the way all these factors affect the expression of mind is essential before we can tackle the problem to which Professor Le Gros Clark has referred, the physical basis for differences in intelligence.

It is unlikely that all this knowledge is going to be obtained from a direct attack on the living organism. There are many pitfalls in exploring mental processes —which in man reveal themselves in the symbols of language—with their self-same mental processes. Fortunately, however, recent developments in electronics allow us to represent at least part of the problem by analogy. Machines can be made—and exist—which exhibit some attributes of mental processes. The most important of these is self-organization—the attainment of a new state of equilibrium with every new piece of experience.

The brain, as Dr. Ashby put it, looks after itself by correcting all deviations from an optimal state, and it can do so by a variety of methods, being flexible about the route but unchanging in its aim. The possibility that a machine could be devised in which this property is linked with a capacity to learn and remember and even to act—let us say, play a game of chess against a human player—has been studied by several scientists. The likelihood that it can rests upon new developments in communication or electronic engineering, in mechanical methods of control, and in statistical mechanics. An American scientist, Dr. Norbert Wiener, has coined the term cybernetics to cover this whole field of interest. It is derived from the same Greek root as our word to govern.

The basic principle of, let us call it, the thinking machine is what is known as a negative feed-back. The simplest instrument which manifests this principle is the thermostat controlling, say, a central heating system. As soon as the temperature exceeds a set figure, the thermostat sends a message back to the control furnace or to a master electrical switch, and the heat is cut off. As soon as the temperature falls below the set figure, the heat is switched on again. In certain types of steering-gear, negative feed-back messages regulate the motion of a ship which is set to follow a given path. More complicated examples of the use of negative feed-back are provided by such modern devices as the automatic pilot of an aircraft, or target-seeking anti-aircraft guns, and target-seeking missiles.

Negative feed-back also controls our muscular actions. We are constantly aware of the position of our muscles and joints through what is called our proprioceptive sense. The physical basis of this sense is almost as well understood as is that of vision. When I reach my hand out to pick up the watch in front of me, every stage of the movement is signalled back—automatically—until the distance between my hand and the watch becomes zero. Of course, my eyes help as well in controlling the movement, but even so the final statement as to whether I have overshot or under-shot must come from my arm and hand. There are diseases in which these automatic adjustments cease to be possible, and the people so afflicted become unstable in their gait, and exhibit tremors—in spite of the fact that they still have their eyes to help them adjust their movements.

The general conclusion to which this points is this. At each moment during the course of a response—whatever its nature—information about the extent to which the response is less than the amount necessary to ensure that the goal is reached is 'fed-back' into the system. The response is thus corrected at each stage of the action to meet the particular needs of the particular movement at that moment—and a type response is converted into a particular response.

Feed-back control occurs not only in postural, visceral, and so-called voluntary activities, but also in all the chemical processes of the body and in the functioning of the hormones. Indeed, these last two exhibit the most obvious self-organizing processes. Thus our bodies have a host of controlling devices which help to maintain a fairly constant internal environment in spite of gross changes outside us. For example, if it is too hot, our internal temperature does not rise—instead we get flushed and sweat and lose heat. And if it is too cold, the blood-vessels in our skin contract, and heat is conserved, and we also start shivering, our muscles so producing heat.

But this feed-back mechanism is only one essential of an automatic brain. The others are a memory system and a capacity for learning and prediction. Now memory—by which we can understand the preservation of past experience for future use—is not confined to living systems. It is also exhibited by ultra-rapid calculating machines. These store the memory of each previous stage of an operation as they go along. This they do through consecutive switching devices or relays, which may operate in an analogous way to nerve cells. In the process of recall, a relay or nerve cell will fire only if it has been sufficiently activated or stimulated by incoming impulses from other relays or neurons.

There are numerous mechanical processes for storing memory—of which photography is perhaps the best known. Another is magnetized tape or wire, which is the principle on which certain new dictaphones operate, or a large series of condensers which can be charged. Memory can be stored in this way for years and years.

Prediction and learning are really an extension of memory, in so far as the trend of previous experience can be projected into the future. I am assured that it is possible to reproduce mechanically the learning mechanism, while prediction is an easy problem for a machine. A machine, for example, can calculate much more quickly than we can the future position of an aeroplane that is flying a certain course at a certain speed. More than that—it can estimate far more quickly the relative probabilities of possible alternatives. But it can do this only for one major task or run at a time. Between tasks it clears itself of all its memories. The run of a human brain lasts an entire lifetime.

To go back a moment. The feed-back mechanism presupposes a perceptual process at the start. The sense organs of a brain-machine would be photo-electric cells, thermometers, microphones, radar scanners, and so on. But perception and learning imply comparison with previous perception if effective use is to be made of a new experience. This means that to be

D

like the human eye, the eye of a machine must not only be able to scan a region that is being explored but also to compare the impressions received with a general—not a particular—perceptual pattern which it has already fixed as memory; and the machine must react one way if there is a correspondence, and another if there is not. This, we are told, is also feasible mechanically. According to some authorities mechanical recognizing devices can be made which will operate independently of the size or orientation of the object viewed—and which therefore perceive relations in the same way as we do.

It is necessary to remember, however, that the pattern of stimuli to which an artificial brain will respond is built into the machine by an external agency during construction. The patterns to which a real brain responds are, on the other hand, established through past experience. A living brain is thus self-organizing, establishing its own connections, its own patterns of memory, and the feed-backs necessary for the maintenance of an equilibrium. The difference between the real and artificial brains is, however, ceasing to be absolute, since machine-brains have been made which, even if in only a rudimentary way, are also dynamically responsible for the establishment and working of their own controls.

Artificial brains would undoubtedly help us understand—by analogy—the physical basis of our own mental processes. There are certainly, however, years and years of study ahead before we can even begin to appreciate the extent of the whole problem. It contains so many questions. Just look at a few—chosen at random. The brain is divided into right and left halves.

In right-handed people mental processes, and memory, are much more disturbed if the left half of the brain is damaged than the right, and it is the other way about in left-handed people. How does this come about? Again, different parts of the uppermost part of the brain—the cerebral cortex—are differentiated anatomically for different functions. Visual impressions, for example, are referred in the first place to the hinder part of the brain. But exactly where and how patterns of visual impression unite, to form master-images—with simultaneous or temporally distinct patterns of other sensory impressions—is a mystery. No one is even sure yet whether intelligence—and the capacity for learning—are general functions of the uppermost layers or cortex of the brain, or attributes of special parts of the cortex. And lastly, why should stirring up the front part of the brain with a probe bring peace and, from the social point of view, some measure of sanity to certain kinds of insane people? To all these things there is certainly a physical basis. What it is may possibly be answered in some broadcasting programme a hundred years from now. But—if I may return to the point I made at the start—I am fairly sure that we are not likely to find out what it is unless we continue to look at mental processes as events which are amenable to strict formulation and proper scientific inquiry.

V

CONSCIOUSNESS

By ELIOT SLATER

THE aspects of the mind I want to consider are consciousness and emotion. When we consider consciousness, there is an error we must beware of. Many people think of consciousness as something that is either there or not there. But it is not like that at all. Hughlings Jackson once said, 'There is no such entity as consciousness—in health we are from moment to moment differently conscious.' Consciousness is to be measured in degrees; and while we only notice the really big changes, as from sleeping to waking, our attention is not caught by the minor fluctuations which are constantly going on.

Consciousness is a state of awareness, and so is absolutely dependent on the information our senses provide about ourselves and about the outside world. Indeed, the awareness we have of our own bodies plays a quite special part. The neurologists have shown that if we are deprived of the sensations we receive from our bodies, in feelings of touch, pressure, movement, and so on, and of our sense of hearing, we become unconscious, even though the senses of sight and smell remain. It is therefore only to be expected that any physical change which affects our senses will affect also, to some extent, our degree of consciousness. Consciousness can only be experienced subjectively, but we have very little idea of how conscious we are. When we are asleep we do not know we sleep; and when we are half-awake we are only dimly aware that all is not as it should be. However, the effects of consciousness can be seen objectively, from outside; and the objective test for consciousness is the complexity and above all the purposiveness of a person's behaviour. We can apply this test even to states which we think of as unconscious, such as sleep. When we are asleep we move about in our beds to prevent our limbs being cramped, and to that extent our actions are purposive, which means we are partly conscious. Indeed, some people are capable of far more purposeful behaviour, anything from talking in their sleep or walking out of bed and back again, to the case of the man who walked out of his house and went fishing.

In our waking life, too, we see all degrees of consciousness. When we first awake, we may be clumsy in our movements; we forget to do things in the right order; it is very easy, for instance, to allow the toast to burn. Some people can wake completely in less than a minute. Others are a little torpid or distrait for any time up to an hour. In the half-way stage between sleep and waking things may happen which do not otherwise occur to the normal man, things like hallucinations. Some people, when they are on the point of going to sleep, see shapes or patterns or even scenes. One of my friends sees such vivid scenes, which change so quickly, that he entertains himself with a sort of cinema show for a few minutes before he drops off.

These changes in the degree of awareness of reality

and in the purposiveness of our behaviour are going on all through the day as well. We know the signs of tiredness and hunger in our husbands, wives, and workmates; but I do not think most people realize that both fatigue and hunger bring an actual, though slight, impairment of consciousness. The hungry man is likely to be irritable, inattentive, edgy; his powers of concentration are not as good as usual. Hunger usually means that the body's stocks of food, especially sugar, are being used up. The concentration of the sugar in the blood drops a little, though very sensitive regulatory mechanisms prevent it from dropping far. We might suppose that these two changes, in the sugar concentration in the blood and in the mental state, were connected. We would be the more likely to think that if we could show that changes in blood sugar did cause some actual change in the brain. There is, in fact, such a change. In the surface areas of the brain electrical changes are constantly going on. Professor Adrian talked about them in his broadcast. They can be picked up by electrodes placed on the scalp, magnified some million times, and recorded on a paper band in a graph. As a rule the graph shows waves of all frequencies, with a dominant wave running at eight to ten cycles a second. If we lower the blood sugar concentration, which we can do experimentally by an injection of insulin, other and slower waves, at five or six cycles a second, are likely to show. The three changes go together—the change in blood chemistry, the change in the electrical activity of the brain, and the change in consciousness.

But this is not the end of the story. People who suffer from the disease of epilepsy are also likely to show changes in the electrical activity of the brain, and among these changes is the appearance of the slow waves I have mentioned. The really interesting thing is that not only epileptics but also some of their relatives may show waves of this nature. For here there is another connection. Epilepsy is a disturbance of consciousness, and epileptics are liable to moods of irritability similar to those shown by the normal but hungry man. Moreover, among the relatives of epileptics will often be found people of unstable temperament, more than normally liable to moods; and it is mainly these unstable relatives who show the peculiar brain waves I have described. The brain waves, consciousness, and behaviour are also liable to interference from other sources. If the blood is made less acid, or, as we say, more alkaline, changes occur in all three. If we wash the carbonic acid out of the blood, by breathing deeply and rapidly for a time, the brain waves change, and we may go dizzy or faint. It is probably because such changes may so easily affect consciousness that the body has developed such sensitive mechanisms of regulating them. The respiratory centre in the brain controls the depth and speed of breathing, so that the blood is maintained always in the same state; and through the liver the blood sugar is controlled. As far as possible, the body tries to cancel out any change in the composition of the blood before it has proceeded more than a very small way.

As in health, so in disease. Many poisons affect consciousness, and we can only suppose that they do so through their effects on brain chemistry. Everyone knows that anaesthetics such as ether can reduce consciousness to vanishing point, and that alcohol has a similar, slighter effect, though a rather more cheerful one. South American Indians intoxicate themselves with moscal, a drug which produces the most vivid hallucinations. The hallucinations are visual, often complexly patterned and brightly coloured—such as of a magnificent Turkey carpet, or marble palaces, or brilliant gardens. Complicated and coloured visual hallucinations may also be seen in epilepsy, but otherwise are rare. The poisons produced by disease may cause changes in consciousness, even to delirium. But much slighter changes are common. People who suffer from tuberculosis sometimes have an unwarrantably cheerful optimism, the 'spesphthisica.' People who are convalescing from influenza sometimes have just the opposite, a severe mood of hopelessness and depression. But these may perhaps be classed as changes in personality rather than a change in consciousness. For though a man may be depressed, we may be unable to show that he is less alert than usual, slower in comprehension, forgetful, or less intelligent.

With temperamental changes we are entering on a difficult topic. There can be nothing more certain than that changes in our moods may be caused psychologically, by ideas, by our understanding of the things that happen to us. But they may also be caused directly and physically. Everyone knows what it is to be anxious—that uncomfortable feeling of shortness of breath and a turning-over of the stomach just before going in to an important interview or making a first appearance in public. The physical and mental parts of this emotion are not to be separated. Presumably the idea in the mind is the first thing to arise. We can regard the whole condition as the spread of stimulation in certain nervous pathways. The stimulation extends to that part of the nervous system which controls the internal organs, and to those organs themselves. One pair of them, the suprarenal glands, secrete into the blood a drug called adrenalin. We know the exact chemical structure of this substance. Its effects are to raise the pressure under which the blood circulates, so that many parts of the body, especially the brain, get a richer supply of blood. The heart has to beat more strongly. The liver gives up its reserves of sugar, and the concentration of sugar in the blood is increased. There are other consequences of the nervous stimulation. The mouth goes dry; the skin becomes pale and sweaty; the muscles become tremulous. When we suffer from anxiety we are aware of these changes, and how unpleasant they are.

This state, the mental and physical state of anxiety, which usually begins as an idea, then shows itself as a physical change, and is finally felt as an unpleasant emotion, may start in a different way. Sometimes a tumour develops in one of the suprarenal glands. Without any special nervous stimulation, the gland secretes a larger amount of adrenalin and discharges it into the blood. The inevitable physical consequences follow; and the patient is aware of an unpleasant emotional state which he cannot put down to any appropriate cause. If physical changes of this nature are lasting ones, they can cause a lasting alteration of the personality. This occurs, above all, with injuries and diseases of the brain. It is much more likely to occur with damage to some parts of the brain than with damage to others. If the occipital lobes, which lie at the back of the head, are injured, there may be a form of blindness, but the personality will not alter much. If the frontal lobes, which lie at the front of the head, are injured, there may not be any specific defect, such as blindness or paralysis, but the personality may suffer. Some men who had head injuries in the war became quite different people after the injury. From being contented they became constantly complaining. Previously energetic, they became listless. At one time placid, after the injury they were upset by mere trifles; or from being good-natured, turned into touchy, irritable, and suspicious people.

If the disease is a progressive one, it may slowly alter the personality out of all recognition. The disease we call general paralysis has this effect. It destroys the highest centres of the brain in a widespread way. Changes in intellect and temperament go hand in hand. Memory becomes faulty; powers of concentration and sustained attention diminish. The first change of temperament may be an exaggeration of its outstanding traits. The moody man becomes moodier, the thin-skinned man still touchier, the boisterous man over-bearing. The patient becomes rather like a caricature of himself. As the disease advances, however, even habitual tendencies become weakened. All the little individualities are washed away, until the man is only recognizable as a patient and no longer as a personality at all. Fortunately, we have very effective methods of treatment of this disease which was once a scourge. The frontal lobes of the brain are concerned very intimately with the control of emotion. The recent method of treatment of mental illness to which Sir Charles Sherrington referred depends on this fact for its success. In those patients who are considered suitable for it a surgical operation is carried out, which divides the fibres connecting the most forwardly placed poles of the brain, right and left, with the rest. A change in personality is caused which is probably permanent. After the operation, the patient is less likely to worry; he takes things more as they come. The tendency to anxiety is reduced. Between stimulus and action there is less deliberation. For those who are over-anxious, who are all too prone to ruminate painfully, the operation may have much to offer. On the other hand, there are disadvantages. Some people become tactless and inconsiderate. So the operation is not done unless the patient's state is such that something must be done, and only this treatment remains to be done.

Let us glance over the ground we have covered. Consciousness and intellectual powers depend above all on the brain, and on its nourishment by blood of exactly the right quality. This is true for all such aspects of consciousness as perception, attention, memory, and reasoning. Injury of the brain or alteration of its blood supply will cause changes in consciousness. Some people have better brains than others, and it is likely that consciousness has a different meaning for the very alert, intelligent man from what it signifies in the very dull and stupid man. The brain, however, is so complex that we have not been able to find a visible difference in the machinery in these two cases. Lenin's brain was examined microscopically in great detail and showed no certain difference from the brains of ordinary men. The brain is also responsible for the conscious aspects of emotion. But emotions have also unconscious or only partly conscious aspects. These are under the control of nervous centres outside the brain and of bodily organs, especially certain glands. Differences in personality between one man and another may lie as much in the organization and regulation of these glands as in the brain itself. A man's personality may be shown, not only in the lines and expression of his face, but even in his skeleton. Psychiatrists are convinced that we find a rather different run of personalities in men of long, thin, and narrow build, from the general type of personalities we find in short and tubby men. In the thin and narrow type we are likely to find anxious people, cool and reserved people, and people who are pedantic and over-meticulous. In the plump, round-faced, and round-bodied we are more likely to find people who are cheerful, sociable, energetic, and interested in the affairs of others. Such mental differences are then likely to have a physical basis, though a basis whose cause is not, perhaps, to be sought in the brain itself.

Our learning, therefore, does not take us very far. And the future that further research will bring us is still vague. I think it very probable that our ideas will have to be completely reorganized. The ambiguities and contradictions which are involved when we make use of such words as 'consciousness,' 'mind,' 'free will,' which now seem so insuperable, may yield to quiet investigation, or may be shown to be but verbal, and the result of our asking ourselves the wrong sort of question. What we already know does, however, suggest that the relationship between body and mind is so intimate that they are best regarded as one. When behaviour reaches a certain degree of complexity it will begin to have a conscious or mental aspect. The lower limits of mind we can see in our infants, in domestic animals, in the sleeping man, and in the mentally affected patient. Of what its upper limits may be we can have no conception.

VI

SPEECH AND THOUGHT

By RUSSELL BRAIN

I AM going to talk about speech and thought. I want
to begin by telling you something about what happens in the brain when we speak, and then go on to
discuss what light that throws upon what happens when
we think. Professor Adrian said in his talk how difficult
it is from the standpoint of *physiology* to conceive of a
way to bridge the gulf between the brain and the mind,
and he pointed out that we must look for progress in
psychology to help us towards a solution of the problem.
It is a parallel advance in physiology and psychology
that we need, and in this talk I am going to try and
show where I think that advance is likely to occur—in
fact, where it has already begun.

I want to attempt to answer this question—are there
functions of the nervous system which are at the same
time both physiological and psychological? I don't
mean by this occurrences like the electrical changes
which can be detected in the back of the brain when
we see, for since we do not know the connection between
the electrical changes and seeing, they take us no
further. But, are there events in the brain which we
can understand as being at the same time both physiological and mental? Now I believe that there are, and
it is in the realm of speech and thought that we shall

find them, even though at the moment they are little more than dim outlines seen through the mist of our ignorance.

As we all know, speech has two sides to it; we listen to speech and we speak ourselves. I shall not have time to say anything about the second aspect of speech, which consists of the utterance of words: I shall have to confine myself to what has been called the receptive side; that is, the understanding of words which we hear and read. This element in speech seems, in fact, to be more closely related to thinking than the means by which we express our thoughts when we have already arrived at them.

I am speaking to you now, and you are listening to me. No doubt it seems to you a very simple process, but, in fact, it is so extremely complicated that it is very difficult to understand. Let us take as an example the word 'dog.' I pronounce the word in one way and you may pronounce it in another. If I were born in Devonshire and you were born in Glasgow, or Bradford, there would be considerable differences in the way in which we should speak, and yet we should understand one another. No two people pronounce the word 'dog' in exactly the same way, yet we always know what it means. Not only that, but I might sing it, or shout it, or whisper it, and it would still convey the same thing to you. The puzzle arises from the fact that each different way of pronouncing 'dog' causes a different electrical disturbance in the nervous system. High-pitched notes go to one spot on the surface of the brain and low-pitched notes go to another which, though not far away, is quite distinct. So if your voice is high-pitched you will start electrical currents moving in one place in my brain, and if it is low-pitched in another, and every variation in the inflection of your voice will produce a different electrical disturbance in the brain of the hearer. And yet he will always hear and understand the same word.

But we can go further than that. Suppose that I had lost my voice and had to write the word 'dog' and show it to you. It will still *mean* the same thing to you though the word no longer consists of sounds, but is made up of black marks on a white piece of paper; you will still be able to understand it, whether it is written or printed, in large or small letters, in black or coloured type, and in any sort of handwriting short of complete illegibility: in many handwritings the marks that people make on the paper have very little resemblance to the letters they are supposed to represent. Here, then, there is as great a variety among the visual patterns presented to the nervous system as among spoken words. Moreover, the patterns of things we see send electrical impulses to a different part of the brain from that which is concerned with hearing. The brain's quite separate centres for the sense of touch can also be brought in. If you can read braille, you will be able to recognize a series of raised pimples on the paper, which make a pattern quite unlike ordinary letters, and yet also mean the word 'dog.'

Now we know that in the brain there is a complicated set of nervous pathways, like a whole series of electrical circuits, which are thrown into activity whenever we think of the meaning of the word 'dog'; and there are different sets of nervous pathways for other words. The problem, therefore, is to explain how a single set of pathways, those concerned with the meaning of the word 'dog,' can be selected from all the others and set going by any one of that indefinitely large number of different groups of sounds and patterns on paper which constitute all the possible ways of saying, or writing, or printing the word so that it can be understood. When I dial an automatic telephone exchange I ask it a question to which I hope to receive an accurate answer, namely, the subscriber to whom I wish to speak, but the machine is very particular about the way in which I put the question. If I want Whitehall 1212, I must dial WHI 1212 and nothing else. No machine has been designed which will answer with Whitehall 1212 if I or anyone else *speak* the words and figures into the mouthpiece. Only the human brain can do this. Until the dialling machine was designed to standardize the way the question is asked, the human brain of the telephone operator had to be employed at the exchange. Now I do not think it is theoretically impossible to design a machine which could answer fairly accurately to the spoken voice, but I suspect that if it ever is made it will have to embody the same principles upon which the human brain works.

Perhaps, after all, the automatic telephone does provide a clue to what happens in the brain. What the dialling apparatus does is to convert the letters and figures of the telephone number into a certain pattern of electrical impulses in time and space, which is different for each number. What the brain does with the spoken word—and no one can say how it does it— is to extract from it an electrical pattern in time and space which is distinctive of the word 'dog,' and common to all the ways in which it can be pronounced, so as to be recognized. It is as though the meaning of the

E

word were locked up in a cupboard which had to be opened by a key. The curious thing is that it is possible to open it by a very large number of keys which superficially seem to be very different from one another. But what makes a key open a lock is a certain kind of pattern. The pattern of the key must be appropriate to the pattern of the lock, and if it is appropriate it does not matter whether the key is made of brass, or steel, or silver, or even gold. In the brain the patterns are very complicated electrical ones. All the possible ways of pronouncing the word 'dog' so that it can be understood have something in common; that is, a certain pattern of sound. This in turn is capable of exciting in the nervous system its own particular pattern of nervous circuits, and this constitutes the key that unlocks the door which contains the meaning of the word. In somewhat the same way all the different ways of writing or printing the word 'dog' arouse a common pattern in a different part of the brain and this also fits the lock of the meaning.

All this complex process goes on in our brains without our knowing anything about it. We hear or read the word and we know what it means, but we know nothing at first hand about the processes which form the link between the two. Sometimes we lose the key either temporarily or, as a result of disease, permanently. You have forgotten someone's name: let us suppose it is 'Johnson': I ask you if it is Smith, Brown, or Robinson, and you reject all these. 'Is it Johnson?' I say, and you say at once, 'Yes, that is it!' When you did not know what the name was, how did you know it was not Smith, Brown, or Robinson? Because these keys did not fit the lock, and when I offered you Johnson it fitted and at once you realized that that was the key you had lost. This illustrates the point that there are processes in the recognition of words of which we are not conscious. What I have called the lock must be unconscious, for you used the Johnson lock to test the key, yet your possession of the lock did not by itself enable you to remember the name.

Now let us turn to thought and consider an abstract idea: let us choose the idea of triangularity. A rat can be trained to recognize a triangle and distinguish it from a square or a circle; such a rat may be said to be aware of triangularity. The process in the nervous system by means of which a rat recognizes a triangle is of the same kind as that by which a human being recognizes a word. The pattern of excitement aroused in the rat's nervous system by all sorts of triangles has something in common which is distinct from that aroused by other geometrical figures, and this common pattern influences the rat's behaviour.

It would be possible to teach a child to recognize a triangle in the same way as a rat is taught. A child might be shown a variety of figures and given a chocolate when it chose a triangle and a punishment when it chose anything else. But since we can speak to a child we can take a short cut and say, 'A triangle is a figure bounded by three straight lines.' We shall then have to use words to enable the child to grasp an abstract idea. But we must not forget that someone must have had the idea of a triangle before it could be described in words. So speech and thought interact. If we are to name something, the nervous system must be capable of recognizing a common pattern in a number of different objects; and, when an object has

already been named, this in itself helps us to detect
what it has in common with other objects of the same
name. We can get along very well in simple matters
without using words for our thinking, but as soon as
we have to think about things which are not concrete
objects we find it difficult to think without words. If
you go into a room and find the cat on the table
drinking the milk, you take in the situation and act
appropriately without formulating, even in your own
mind, the words 'cat,' 'table,' and 'milk,' though you
would have to do so if you wanted to draw the attention
of someone else to what was happening. But listen to
this sentence from Plato: 'Can there be any greater evil
in the state than discord and distraction and plurality
where unity ought to reign?' We cannot think about
the ideas contained in that sentence without using
words for the purposes of our thought.

I have spoken earlier about the meaning of a word.
Without going into the much-debated philosophical
question of the meaning of meaning I want to point
out that we use the term meaning in at least two
different ways. Let us take as an example a proper
name—'St. Paul's Cathedral.' In one sense these
words mean—that is, they refer to—a certain building in
London. But in another sense, when I say that I know
what they mean I am saying that they enable me to
think of that building, and what I think of it will
depend upon my past experience of it. If I have seen
it I shall perhaps form a mental picture of its dome
rising above London. If not, I may think of a service
broadcast from it, or of Harrison Ainsworth's novel,
Old St. Paul's, or of the cathedral of which John Donne
was dean. Any or all of these are, as we put it, what

St. Paul's Cathedral *means* to me. So in this sense the meaning of a word implies its power to awaken in us all kinds of past associations, ideas, and feelings, and sometimes memory-images, and these must depend upon numerous and widespread pathways irradiating over the surface and deep into the substance of the brain. Yet clearly we can speak the word and know what it means without calling up any of these associations, so that often in conversation the words 'St. Paul's Cathedral' just stand for all these potential associations without necessarily making us conscious of any of them. We are able to do this because there exists in the brain an electrical pattern for each word which is not identical with those underlying either its sound or its meaning.

Here we have reached the foundation of all language —the fact that a word can stand for the concrete thing or the abstract idea which it represents. But the value —and also the danger—of words for the purposes of thought is that though they are linked with their meanings we can deal with them as though they were relatively independent of them. We treat them as counters, or bank-notes, or cheques, so that, as the philosopher Leibniz put it, we can perform complicated operations with them and wait until these operations are concluded before converting the results into coins. But words would be useless for thinking if they did not retain below the surface of our minds their links with their meanings; and it was the constant task of Socrates, as it is of philosophers to-day, to persuade people to examine the meanings of the words they use.

Now let me try and sum up what I have said. All stimuli, whether sights, sounds, or other sensations, reach the brain as electrical patterns, and it seems to be a basic function of the nervous system to analyse these patterns so as to detect similarity amidst differences. A rat can distinguish a triangle from other geometrical figures, and this is the beginning of abstract thought. We do the same thing with words. The word 'dog' for the nervous system is not simply any of the thousand and one ways in which it can be pronounced: it is also an electrical pattern which is called up by each and all of them and of which we are not even conscious. The function of this electrical pattern is to arouse other patterns—those underlying ideas, feelings, and perhaps memory-images, which is what the word means to us and through which we know what it refers to. We can think to some extent without words, but only in rather a concrete way: we cannot entertain abstract ideas without using them. But when we think with words we often use them, like counters, to stand for things or ideas, in order to save ourselves the trouble of having to think every time about the things or ideas themselves. To that extent we are all like the little girl who was told to think before she spoke and replied: 'But how can I know what I think till I hear what I say?'

Is it likely that physiology will ever throw any real light upon the relationship between the brain and the mind? I believe that, working in conjunction with psychology, it will; but you must not expect me to give you a clear idea of how that will happen. I can only guess where present advances seem to be leading us. Think of a pattern. An atom is a pattern of electrons, a molecule is a pattern of atoms. There are patterns of patterns of patterns, and so on indefinitely. The most complicated patterns we know are in the brain. Not only are there twelve thousand million nerve cells out of which the patterns can be made, but nervous patterns exist in time, like a melody, as well as in space. If you look at a tapestry through a magnifying glass you will see the individual threads but not the pattern: if you stand away from it you will see the pattern but not the threads. My guess is that in the nervous system we are looking at the threads while with the mind we perceive the patterns, and that one day we shall discover how the patterns are made out of the threads.

VII

THE CEREBRAL CORTEX AND THE MIND OF MAN

By WILDER PENFIELD

SOME of you may raise eyebrows in surprise that a neurosurgeon should presume to consider so abstract a problem as the physical basis of the mind. But I may point out that addiction to the use of the scalpel did not exclude the founder of neurosurgery, Sir Victor Horsley, nor his pupil, Wilfred Trotter, from such preoccupations. And to-day it does not prevent Geoffrey Jefferson of Manchester and Hugh Cairns of Oxford from contributing with distinction to this field of thought.

Years ago Sir Charles Sherrington demonstrated to his students, of whom I was one, delicate reflexes which are responsible for automatic movements of animals. Such things as withdrawal of a foot from a painful contact, stepping, and standing are carried out by automatic reflex action through nerves, spinal cord, and lower brain stem. The mind of a man, like that of an animal for that matter, is something that we cannot see or touch or stimulate. It is the faculty which is responsible for that portion of human behaviour which does not seem to be automatic.

Men and women who have some minor affection of the brain can tell us a great deal about the mind. It is this information in my own experience as a brain surgeon that I shall draw upon here. It is not so far a cry from the brain of a monkey to the brain of a man. The two individuals do not think alike, and I suspect that the monkey would always enrol himself with the opposition if he could; but the mechanisms of the two nervous systems are alike, and many a man has been freed from some affliction because of the experiments of Sherrington and Adrian upon laboratory monkeys.

Everyone knows that the mind of a man is something that depends upon the action of the brain. Things are seen, heard, felt, or smelt only when electrical currents are conducted along appropriate nerve tracts to the brain. Problems are worked out by using the brain. A voluntary act is dictated somehow at a high level of organization within the cranial cavity. Then executive messages are flashed down the spinal cord and out along the nerves, and action through muscular contraction follows with amazing speed and dexterity. Everyone knows, too, that a blow upon the head may put an end to feeling, action, thought. The man, upon whose unlucky shoulders that head was resting, becomes unconscious. The action of the brain is arrested by the blow, and so the mind does not exist for the time being. All this is the commonest of common knowledge. Shakespeare was aware of these things when he referred to the 'brain which some suppose the soul's frail dwelling house.'

What can we say about the mechanisms within that 'dwelling house'? There are in it millions of nerve cells, or neurones, each provided with long nerve fibres capable of conducting electrical impulses. Each nerve cell sends out such impulses. It is obvious that there must be a co-ordinating centre within the 'house,' a

sort of telephone exchange or switchboard to which
messages come, and from which messages depart after
appropriate decisions are reached, decisions that are
based upon memories of previous experience and
influenced by present desires.

The brain is a large spherical organ that is divided
into two partially separated halves, the right and the
left hemispheres. A superficial layer of nerve cells
covers the whole of the cerebral hemispheres in an
outer mantle of grey matter. This is the cerebral bark,
or cortex. The most striking difference between the
brain of man and that of other animals, which we refer
to as lower than ourselves, is the enormous development
of cerebral cortex which is found in man. It covers the
convolutions and folds itself down deeply into the
fissures that separate the convolutions. Thus, there is
actually more of the cortex within the fissures than
there is on the surface. This increased development of
the cortex of man as compared with that of the lower
animals is particularly great in the frontal lobes that
occupy the front part of the skull. For example, even
when we allow for the difference in size of the cat brain
and the human brain, man has eight times more cortex
in the anterior frontal region than his feline friend.
The shape of his forehead bears testimony to this.
Whether man makes good use of this cellular endow-
ment is another story. Perhaps the cat has an adverse
opinion regarding this point. However, these facts have
led to the assumption that the co-ordinating and
controlling centre of man's brain, the switchboard, is
situated within the new brain in the recently evolved
cerebral cortex. But this assumption is actually without
any justification in fact.

There is another enormous assemblage of nerve cells within the brain. It lies in the grey matter of the old brain, which is called the thalamus, and the midbrain. This is placed in a central position deep within the hemispheres. This accumulation of grey matter I shall refer to as the upper brain stem. It is endowed with the lines of communication which are prerequisite to the establishment of any headquarters. There are adequate nerve fibre connections between it and the whole cortex of both hemispheres and with the 'trunk-line' fibre tracts of the lower brain stem and spinal cord. Injury to this area, even an injury of small extent, seriously interferes with understanding, or more often produces deep unconsciousness. Large injuries confined to the cortex do not abolish consciousness, and we have learned that many areas of cortex can be removed with relative impunity.

The cortex covers the surface of the two hemispheres with a mosaic of functional areas. One area is devoted to vision, another to hearing, another to the sense of touch, another to movement of arm or leg, and still others to skills of hand and skills of mouth, such as speaking. The mosaic of the cortex of the right hemisphere is the mirror image of that of the left. All of these areas have connection with the upper brain stem. Almost all inward flowing currents of sensation may be said to go to the cortex for elaboration and then on to the upper brain stem. Only pain sensation goes directly to headquarters without a detour to the cortex. Thus, the cortex is sub-divided into distinct areas which serve the purposes of different functions. The large sheet of cortex which covers the front part of the brain seems to be utilized by man when he is thinking of new plans and seeking greater insight into life's problems. This is the portion of the brain which the cat might consider quite unnecessary. Psychiatrists have apparently reached the same conclusion, for during the last few years they have made the operation of leucotomy fashionable as a cure for the anxiety of some patients who are insane and for others who are not so insane. This operation, which amputates both frontal lobes, does not produce loss of memory because other parts of the cortex are used for the recording of memory; and no interference is produced with sensory perception nor with motor control, for a similar reason. But the luckless individual does forfeit capacity for planned initiative. He may have gained peace of mind but he has lost a type of insight that is difficult to define.

In the treatment of certain conditions, especially focal epilepsy, it becomes necessary for the neurosurgeon to expose a patient's cerebral cortex under local anaesthesia. Thus, the subject comes to lie quietly on the operating table, fully conscious, while the surgeon proceeds with his task. It may be advisable to stimulate the cortex with a gentle electrical current. Such stimulation is able to activate certain areas of the cortex. In different sensory areas it causes the individual to feel a tingling in hand or foot; or he may seem to see gross lights, hear simple sounds, or smell crude odours. When an electrode is applied to the motor convolution in the central region of the cortex, movement results in the opposite arm or leg or face. The jaw may move up and down, the throat may swallow, the mouth may open while the patient vocalizes in a long drawn-out tone. Or the eyelids may open and the two eyes turn in unison as though looking upwards or across to the opposite side. As far as the patient is concerned, these movements are irresistible. When the electrode is applied, for example, to the motor area of the right hemisphere, he cannot, by the exercise of his will, prevent his left hand from moving, but he can reach over with the other hand and thus hold the moving member still. When he does this, he doubtless makes use of the motor area in the cortex of the untouched hemisphere. The effector mechanism employed by him during voluntary activity is denied him in one cortex but is still available to him in the other.

There are still more complicated mechanisms, which he must employ when he visualizes the movement of his free hand and when he starts the hand on its projected mission of finding and holding still its helpless counterpart on the opposite side of the body. These mechanisms depend upon mechanisms within the upper brain stem. But these mechanisms must in turn employ the functional activity of various cortical areas with which the brain stem has direct connection.

In occasional cases of focal epilepsy there is chronic irritation of the cortex on the side beneath the temple and the ear. This is the temporal lobe. The irritation seems to sensitize the grey matter of that cortex so much that the surgeon's electrode may reveal the true nature of this region, although under ordinary circumstances stimulation has no obvious effect. In such conditions, stimulation may awaken a memory or cause the patient to experience a dream that is made up of materials from the storehouse of his memory. And yet, during the dream that is thus produced, he may retain some hold on the reality of his environment. While it is going on, he may say to the surgeon, 'Wait and I'll tell you.' Then, after the electrode is withdrawn, he describes the experience. For instance: 'I was in my mother's house. My sisters and mother were there. Everyone was talking.'

Thus, the patient could talk with understanding even while he was having a dream that came to him as the result of artificial activation of neurone patterns, patterns that had been formed in the cortex of one temporal lobe during past experience. Other evidence has suggested that the similar cortex of the opposite hemisphere contains duplicate recordings of memory patterns. Now, if the individual were to recall, voluntarily, the appearance of his mother's living-room, we may surmise that he would activate the same pattern of cortical nerve cell connections. But he would be activating it from within.

Let us consider the situation of the patient a little further. Action that is produced by electrical stimulation of the cortex is so gross, so lacking in dexterity, that it may be likened to the sound of a piano when its keyboard is struck with the palm of the hand. Skilled finger movement can only be elicited from the precentral gyrus when it is played upon by impulses that come to it in the normal manner from a level within the brain that is functionally higher than the convolutions itself. A man who is able to play the piano has a perfect memory pattern of a concerto stored away in his cerebral cortex. He has also acquired the conditioned reflexes of piano playing. When he begins to play there must pass from the upper brain stem to the various motor elements within his motor cortex a series of impulses which cause the fingers to move skilfully over the keyboard. When someone else listens to the concerto, he, or she, hears music that resembles the auditory memory pattern within the player's cortex. The player also listens to his own performance and he compares it with this memory record. If a wrong note is struck, he may stop the playing and begin it over again. When someone else watches the fingers of the player, he sees the motor performance which is made possible by skilled use of the cortical motor apparatus. If an electrophysiologist, or physicist, could apply a sufficiently delicate galvanometer to the motor cortex of the player, he might even record the series of nervous impulses that reach the cortex. That series of impulses would constitute an electronic pattern of the concerto!

Thus, I am suggesting that the master motor area, in the brain of man, may be found at the level of the upper brain stem where sensory information of finger position is available, where the visual image of the piano is available, where the memory of the music is available, as well as the auditory effect, and where conscious control is exerted upon the mechanisms of movement. Such a headquarters switchboard as that is so delicate, so complicated, as to stagger the imagination, but the evidence is overwhelming that it does exist. And it is the seat of consciousness which Herbert Spencer defined as 'that nervous centre to which mediately or immediately the most heterogeneous impressions are brought.' It would seem that the place is in the upper brain stem. But it can only function properly by the simultaneous employment of the various areas of the cortex, each contributing to a different aspect of mental activity. In a sense, therefore, the higher brain stem, together with that portion of the cortex which is being employed at the moment, is the seat of consciousness.

It is the 'physical basis of the mind,' this hypothetical mechanism of nerve cell connections. When a man is conscious, one may conceive that within his brain impulses are passing along a million insulated nerve fibres that compose this complex, impulses that are somehow co-ordinated into the orderly sequences of deliberate thought.

What is the real relationship of this mechanism to the mind? Can we visualize a spiritual element of different essence capable of controlling this mechanism? When a patient is asked about the movement which he carries out as the result of cortical stimulation, he never is in any doubt about it. He knows he did not will the action. He knows there is a difference between automatic action and voluntary action. He would agree that something else finds its dwelling-place between the sensory complex and the motor mechanism, that there is a switchboard operator as well as a switchboard.

VIII

THE PHYSICAL BASIS OF MIND: A PHILOSOPHERS' SYMPOSIUM

I

By THE RT. HON. VISCOUNT SAMUEL

IN so short a broadcast, I can only offer baldly my own conclusions on the question debated in this most interesting, and indeed exciting, discussion, without attempting any survey of the previous contributions.

The discussion has been an approach, from the side of physiology, to one of the oldest and most fundamental of the problems of philosophy—the relation between mind and matter. For centuries, philosophers of different schools have made strenuous efforts to resolve one into the other. Some have sought to show that mind is nothing more than an emanation, in the course of evolution, from matter; others that matter is nothing more than a concept of mind, which alone is real. Those efforts have been unsuccessful: neither view has won general assent.

The materialists appear to ignore the obvious lessons of daily experience. We see, every moment, events which cannot be accounted for by derivations, however subtle, from physical or chemical processes. Watch a chess-player deliberating for a quarter of an hour whether to move his queen here or a pawn there. At last he stretches out his hand and does the one or the other: or he may do neither; using his vocal organs, he may say, 'I resign this game.' The physiologist may reveal the nervous and muscular mechanism which operates the hand or the tongue, but not the process which has decided the player's action. Or consider a novelist making up a story, a musician writing a symphony, a scientist engaged in a mathematical calculation; or, indeed, something much simpler, a bird building its nest, and choosing the right materials for each stage; or a cat waiting for a pause in the traffic before crossing the street. All these, and all such, are engaged in some process that is different in kind from electrical attractions and repulsions, or from the processes that unite particles into atoms, atoms into molecules, molecules into objects, and move them about relatively to one another.

The idealists do not account for the fact, which we are bound to accept from astronomy, geology, and anthropology—if we think at all, and if we accept anything at all—that the stars and the planets and this earth existed aeons before man existed; that the universe carried on its activities then—and may properly be assumed to carry them on now—independently of man's perceiving and observing, timing and measuring. The material universe cannot, therefore, be a product of human thought. If it is said that matter may still be an emanation of mind—the mind of God —that is merely an evasion, removing the problem outside the scope of the argument.

The whole effort—to resolve mind into matter or else matter into mind—is the outcome of what T. H. Green called 'the philosophic craving for unity.' But a craving is something irrational, and we had better beware of becoming addicts. What ground is there for requiring any such unification, either of the one kind or of the other? An essential duality in nature is the alternative that is left.

For those who have proceeded on that assumption, it has been natural and usual to regard the living conscious body as the province of mind and the outside material universe as the province of matter. This series of addresses, which is now concluding, has been most valuable in showing that that is an error; it has put the boundary between the two in the wrong place. The eminent scientists who have taken part in it have clearly established that the acceptance of sense stimuli, the transmission of their effects along the nerve fibres, and their activation of different parts of the brain, are mechanical. Whether the approach is from bio-physics or bio-chemistry, anatomy or pathology, the conclusion is the same—these are material activities, obeying mechanical laws. Dr. Russell Brain who spoke on 'Speech and Thought' tells us that 'all stimuli reach the brain as electrical patterns'; Professor Le Gros Clark and others describe with great clarity the mechanism of the nervous system as a whole. We must conclude that these processes, although inside the body, are not essentially different from the physical processes that are going on outside; rather they are a continuation. When we feel an electric shock, the nerve fibres that carry the current are performing a function similar in kind to that of the copper wire between the battery and the hand. When we hear a sound, the mechanism of the auditory organs, including the relevant part of the brain, is specialized, no doubt, but is not fundamentally of a different order from the air-waves which had carried the sound. It follows that the meeting-place between mind and matter in our own experience is not where we had supposed it to be; it is not at the boundary between body and not-body, but is internal.

That, however, does not solve the problem; it merely shifts it. Some meeting-place there must be to account for the brain-mind relation. And we are bound to assume that, although the two are of different orders, they must have something in common, because there is a meeting-place; because the two interconnect and interact; because body (including brain) does in fact condition and influence mind, and mind does in fact condition and influence body.

The painter or sculptor is conditioned and influenced by his materials; the composer by the musical instruments that exist in his time; the architect by the available building materials; the craftsman by his tools; the captain and crew by their ship. But also the artist, composer, architect, craftsman, or navigator chooses the things that he will use and decides the purposes that they shall serve. So with mind and body.

This discussion has helped to clarify the whole problem by establishing the fact that the meeting-place is not at the points where external stimuli impinge upon the nervous system; it is at the points where mind accepts and utilizes the sense-data offered by the brains But the discussion has not been able to answer the question what it is that takes over at those points; and therefore it could not even begin to consider how the connection may be made.

Here again our scientists are substantially agreed. Professor Le Gros Clark said at the end of his broadcast: 'No more than the physiologist is the anatomist

able even to suggest how the physico-chemical phenomena associated with the passage of nervous impulses
from one part of the brain to another can be translated
into a mental experience.' Dr. Penfield compares the
mechanism of nerve-cell connections to a telephone
switchboard. He asks: 'What is the real relationship
of this mechanism to the mind?' He says that 'there is
a difference between automatic action and voluntary
action: . . . that something else finds its dwelling-place
between the sensory complex and the motor mechanism, that there is a switchboard operator as well as a
switchboard.' Sir Charles Sherrington has written
elsewhere, 'That our being should consist of *two* fundamental elements offers, I suppose, no greater inherent
improbability than that it should rest on onc only.'
Again, 'We have to regard the relation of mind to
brain as still not merely unsolved, but still devoid of a
basis for its very beginning.' And he has ended his
stimulating contribution to the present discussion by
saying, 'Aristotle, 2,000 years ago, was asking how is
the mind attached to the body? We are asking that
question still.'

That, it seems, is where we are now at a standstill.
Until science and philosophy can help us to move on
from that position we cannot hope that the universe
will, for us, be rationalized.

II

By A. J. AYER

I WONDER if Lord Samuel has made it completely clear exactly what the problem is that the philosophers are here called upon to solve? The scientists who have spoken in this series have shown very fully and convincingly how various mental processes—thinking, feeling, perceiving, remembering—are causally dependent upon processes in the brain, but to some of them at least the character of this connection still appears mysterious. Thus, Sir Charles Sherrington remarks that 'it is a far cry from an electrical reaction in the brain to suddenly seeing the world around one, with all its distances, colours, and chiaroscuro'; and Professor Adrian confesses to the same 'misgivings' when he says that 'the part of the picture of the brain which may always be missing is of course the part which deals with the mind, the part which ought to explain how a particular pattern of nerve impulses can produce an idea; or the other way round, how a thought can decide which nerve cells are to come into action.'

If this is a genuine problem, it is hard to see why further information about the brain should be expected to solve it. For however much we amplify our picture of the brain, it remains still a picture of something physical, and it is just the question how anything physical can interact with something that is not that is supposed to constitute our difficulty. If what we are seeking is a bridge across a seemingly impassable river it will not help us merely to elevate one of the banks. It looks, indeed, as if some of the previous speakers were hoping to discover in the brain something describable as the locus of the mind; as if mind and brain could be conceived as meeting at a point in space or as somehow shading into one another: but to me this is not even an intelligible hypothesis. What would it be like to come upon this junction? By what signs would you recognize it if you found it? Descartes had the same problem, and he met it by suggesting that mind and body came together in the pineal gland; but how this conjecture could conceivably be tested he did not explain. The reason he had the problem—the reason why we have it still—is that matter and mind were conceived by him from the outset as distinct orders of being; it is as if there were two separate worlds, such that every event had to belong to one or other of them, but no event could belong to both. But from these premisses it follows necessarily that there can be no bridge or junction; for what would the bridge consist of? Any event that you discovered would have to fall on one or other side of it. So, if there is a difficulty here, it is not because our factual information is scanty, but because our logic is defective. Perhaps this whole manner of conceiving the distinction between mind and matter is at fault. In short, our problem is not scientific but philosophical.

Let us consider, then, what can be meant by saying that a particular pattern of nerve impulses 'produces' an idea, or that 'a thought decides' which nerve cells are to come into action. What are the facts on which such assertions are based? The facts are that the physiologist makes certain observations, and that these observations fall into different categories. On the one hand there are the observations which lead him to tell his story about nerve cells and electrical impulses. That is to say, the story is an interpretation of the observations in question. On the other hand there are the observations which he interprets by saying that the subject of his experiment is in such and such a 'mental' state, that he is thinking, or resolving to perform some action, or feeling some sensation, or whatever it may be. It is then found to be the case that these two sorts of observations can be correlated with one another; that whenever an observation of the first type can be made, there is good reason to suppose that an observation of the second type can be made also. For example, when the scientists make observations which they interpret by saying that such and such nerve cells are undergoing such and such electrical disturbances, they can also make observations which are interpreted by saying that the subject is having sensations of a certain type. Again, when they are able to make such observations as are interpreted by saying that the subject is resolving to perform some action, they can also make further observations which are interpreted by saying that certain impulses are passing through certain of his nerve fibres. It seems to me that when it is asserted that the two events in question—the mental and the physical—are causally connected, that the pattern of nerve impulses 'produces' the sensation, or that the thought 'decides' which nerve cells are to operate, all that is meant, or at least all that can properly be meant, is that these two sets of observations are correlated in the way that I have described. But if this is so, where is the difficulty? There is nothing especially mysterious about the fact that two different sets of observations are correlated; that, given the appropriate conditions, they habitually accompany one another. You may say that this fact requires an explanation; but such an explanation could only be some theory from which the fact of this correlation could be deduced. And in so far as the theory was not a mere redescription of the facts which it was intended to explain, it would serve only to fit them into a wider context. We should learn from it that not only were these observations correlated, but certain further types of observation were correlated with them. To ask *why* something occurs, if it is not simply equivalent to asking *how* it occurs, is to ask what other things are associated with it. Once the facts are fully described, there is no mystery left.

If there seems to be a mystery in this case, it is because we are misled by our conceptual systems; not by the facts themselves but by the pictures which we use to interpret the facts. The physiologist's story is complete in itself. The characters that figure in it are nerve cells, electrical impulses, and so forth. It has no place for an entirely different cast, of sensations, thoughts, feelings, and the other *personae* of the mental play. And just because it has no place for them they do not intervene in it. The muddle arises from trying to make them intervene, as I am afraid Lord Samuel does. We then get a confused, indeed an unintelligible, story of electrical impulses being transmuted into sensations, or of mental processes interleaved with disturbances of the nervous cells. The picture we are given is that of messengers travelling through the brain, reaching a mysterious entity called the mind, receiving orders from it, and then travelling on. But since the mind has no position in space—it is by definition not the sort of thing that can have a position in space—it does not literally make sense to talk of physical signals reaching it; nor are there such temporal gaps in the procession of nervous impulses as would leave room for the mental characters to intervene. In short, the two stories will not mix. It is like trying to play *Hamlet*, not without the Prince of Denmark, but with Pericles, the Prince of Tyre. But to say that the two stories will not mix is not to say that either of them is superfluous. Each is an interpretation of certain phenomena and they are connected by the fact that, in certain conditions, when one of them is true, the other is true also.

My conclusion is, then, that mind and body are not to be conceived as two disparate entities between which we have to make, or find, some sort of amphibious bridge, but that talking about minds and talking about bodies are different ways of classifying and interpreting our experiences. I do not say that this procedure does not give rise to serious philosophical problems; how, for example, to analyse statements about the thoughts and feelings of others; or how far statements about people's so-called mental processes are equivalent to statements about their observable behaviour. But once we are freed from the Cartesian fallacy of regarding minds as immaterial substances, I do not think that the discovery of causal connections between what we choose to describe respectively as mental and physical occurrences implies anything by which we need to be perplexed.

III

By GILBERT RYLE

THE story is told of some peasants who were terrified at the sight of their first railway-train. Their pastor therefore gave them a lecture explaining how a steam-engine works. One of the peasants then said, 'Yes, pastor, we quite understand what you say about the steam-engine. But there is really a horse inside, isn't there?' So used were they to horse-drawn carts that they could not take in the idea that some vehicles propel themselves.

We might invent a sequel. The peasants examined the engine and peeped into every crevice of it. They then said, 'Certainly we cannot see, feel, or hear a horse there. We are foiled. But we know there is a horse there, so it must be a ghost-horse which, like the fairies, hides from mortal eyes.'

The pastor objected, 'But, after all, horses themselves are made of moving parts, just as the steam-engine is made of moving parts. You know what their muscles, joints, and blood-vessels do. So why is there a mystery in the self-propulsion of a steam-engine, if there is none in that of a horse? What do you think makes the horse's hooves go to and fro?' After a pause a peasant replied, 'What makes the horse's hooves go is four extra little ghost-horses inside.'

Poor simple-minded peasants! Yet just such a story has been the official theory of the mind for the last three very scientific centuries. Several, though not all, of the scientists in this series have automatically posed their problem in this very way. I think that Lord

Samuel still accepts the whole story, and that Professor Ayer would like to reject it, but does not see how to do so. For the general terms in which the scientists have set their problem of mind and body, we philosophers have been chiefly to blame, though we have been obsessed, not by the rustic idea of horses, but by the newer idea of mechanical contrivances. The legend that we have told and sold runs like this. A person consists of two theatres, one bodily and one non-bodily. In his Theatre A go on the incidents which we can explore by eye and instrument. But a person also incorporates a second theatre, Theatre B. Here there go on incidents which are totally unlike, though synchronized with those that go on in Theatre A. These Theatre B episodes are changes in the states, not of bits of flesh, but of something called 'consciousness,' which occupies no space. Only the proprietor of Theatre B has first-hand knowledge of what goes on in it. It is a secret theatre. The experimentalist tries to open its doors, but it has no doors. He tries to peep through its windows, but it has no windows. He is foiled.

We tend nowadays to treat it as obvious that a person, unlike a newt, lives the two lives, life 'A' and life 'B,' each completely unlike, though mysteriously geared to the other. Ingrained hypotheses do feel obvious, however redundant they may be. The peasants in my story correctly thought that a steam-engine was hugely different from a cart and automatically but incorrectly explained the difference by postulating a ghost-horse inside. So most of us, correctly thinking that there are huge differences between a clock and a person, automatically but incorrectly explain these differences by postulating an extra set of ghost-works inside. We correctly say that people are not like clocks, since people meditate, calculate, and invent things; they make plans, dream dreams, and shirk their obligations; they get angry, feel depressed, scan the heavens, and have likes and dislikes; they work, play, and idle; they are sane, crazy, or imbecile; they are skilful at some things and bunglers at others. Where we go wrong is in explaining these familiar actions and conditions as the operations of a secondary set of secret works.

Everybody knows quite well when to describe someone as acting absent-mindedly or with heed, as babbling deliriously or reasoning coherently, as feeling angry but not showing it, as wanting one thing but pretending to want another, as being ambitious, patriotic, or miserly. We often get our accounts and estimates of other people and of ourselves wrong; but we more often get them right. We did not need to learn the legend of the two theatres before we were able to talk sense about people and to deal effectively with them. Nor has this fairly new-fangled legend helped us to do it better.

When we read novels, biographies, and reminiscences, we do not find the chapters partitioned into Section 'A,' covering the hero's 'bodily' doings, and Section 'B,' covering his 'mental' doings. We find unpartitioned accounts of what he did and thought and felt, of what he said to others and to himself, of the mountains he tried to climb and the problems he tried to solve. Should an examiner mark the paper written by the candidate's hand but refuse to assess the candidate's wits? Theorists themselves, when actually describing people, sensibly forget Theatre A and Theatre B. Sir

Charles Sherrington paid a well-deserved compliment to Professor Adrian, but he did not pay one cool compliment to Professor Adrian 'A' and another warmer compliment to Professor Adrian 'B.'

In saying that a person is not to be described as a mind coupled with a body I am not saying, with some truculent thinkers, that people are just machines. Nor are engines just wagons or live bodies just corpses. What is wrong with the story of the two theatres is not that it reports differences which are not there but that it misrepresents differences which are there. It is a story with the right characters but the wrong plot. It is an attempt to explain a genuine difference—or rather a galaxy of differences—but its effect, like that of the peasants' theory, is merely to reduplicate the thing to be explained. It says, 'The difference between a machine like a human body on the one hand and a human being on the other is that in a human being, besides the organs which we do see, there is a counterpart set of organs which we do not see; besides the causes and effects which we can witness, there is a counterpart series of causes and effects which we cannot witness.' So now we ask, 'But what explains the differences between what goes on in the Theatre B of a sane man and what goes on in that of a lunatic? A third theatre, Theatre C?'

No, what prevents us from examining Theatre B is not that it has no doors or windows, but that there is no such theatre. What prevented the peasants from finding the horse was not that it was a ghost-horse, but that there was no horse. None the less, the engine *was* different from a wagon and ordinary people *are* different not only from machines, but also from animals, imbeciles, infants, and corpses. They also differ in countless important ways from one another. I have not begun to show how we should grade these differences. I have only shown how we should not grade them.

One last word. In ordinary life (save when we want to sound knowing) we seldom use the noun 'Mind' or the adjective 'mental' at all. What we do is to talk of people, of people calculating, conjuring, hoping, resolving, tasting, bluffing, fretting, and so on. Nor, in ordinary life, do we talk of 'Matter' or of things being 'material.' What we do is to talk of steel, granite, and water; of wood, moss, and grain; of flesh, bone, and sinew. The umbrella-titles 'Mind' and 'Matter' obliterate the very differences that ought to interest us. Theorists should drop both these words. 'Mind' and 'Matter' are echoes from the hustings of philosophy and prejudice the solutions of all problems posed in terms of them.